The Landscape of the
BRONTËS

The Landscape of the
BRONTËS

ARTHUR POLLARD

With photographs by Simon McBride

Grange BOOKS

Frontispiece: Ponden Kirk. Looking down Ponden Clough with Haworth Moor on right.

First published in Great Britain 1988 by
Webb & Bower (Publishers) Limited
9 Colleton Crèscent, Exeter, Devon EX2 4BY
in association with Michael Joseph Limited
27 Wright's Lane, London W8 5TZ

Designed by Vic Giolitto

Production by Nick Facer/Rob Kendrew

Text Copyright © 1988 Arthur Pollard

Photographs Copyright © 1988 Simon McBride

Published by Grange Books
An Imprint of Books & Toys Limited
The Grange
Grange Yard
LONDON   SE1   3AG

ISBN: 1·85627·240·0

This edition published 1992
Printed by: Gráficas Reunidas, Ş.A. (Madrid)

Contents

Preface

A landscape ceases to be merely topographical when there are people in it. When those people are the Brontë sisters, the landscape is far more than topographical. It becomes a literary landscape, but the literature cannot be fully appreciated without the topography nor, in the case of these sisters, something of their biography. To understand their books we need to know their lives; to understand their lives we need to know where they were spent. The Brontë novels are redolent of the moors that roll away from the bleak upland manufacturing village of Haworth which has become world famous because it was there that these sad sisters and remarkable women passed their days.

In the text that follows I have drawn freely on illustrative passages from the novels and, as every writer on the Brontës must, I have called Charlotte's first and finest biographer, Mrs Gaskell, frequently to my aid. These provide the verbal foundation, Simon McBride's photography the memorable superstructure.

He and I would wish to acknowledge the help we have received, notably from the Council of the Brontë Society, who allowed us liberal access to their treasures; from Dr Juliet Barker, the Librarian of the Brontë Parsonage Museum, whose deep acquaintance with the subject both extended our own knowledge and brought to light new material for this volume; from her colleague, Sally Johnson; and, above all else, from Christine Sumner who gave generously of her time and her unrivalled familiarity with Brontëana detail not only to enable us to share her enthusiasm but also to save this work from inadequacies and error. Needless to say, whatever of these remain must be the responsibility of the author. I should like once again to thank Ruth Green for her immaculate deciphering of my execrable hand.

ARTHUR POLLARD

Introduction:
The Brontë Legend

Shakespeare tells us that 'a sad tale's best for winter': so perhaps winter's best for a sad tale. On her first visit to Haworth Mrs Gaskell came not in winter but in late September, and even then 'It was a dull, drizzly Indian-inky day ... lead-coloured.' On her way she passed ' ... grey dull-coloured rows of stone-cottages ... poor, hungry-looking fields; stone-fences everywhere, and trees nowhere. Haworth is a long, straggling village: one steep narrow street ...' and when she reached the parsonage front door, '... moors everywhere beyond and above. The crowded grave-yard surrounds the house.' (*Life of Charlotte Brontë*, hereafter referred to as *Life*, Chapter 27) The modern visitor will recognize the scene—and the atmosphere.

Why then does he or she and thousands of others come to Haworth? 'To strangers ... who are unacquainted with the locality, ... to whom the inhabitants, the customs ... are things alien and familiar. To all such', Charlotte Brontë wrote in her preface to Emily's *Wuthering Heights*, 'the wild moors of the north of England can for them have no interest.' How wrong she has proved to be!

The reason for her error is the legend which she herself (and Emily) played such a large part in creating, so that what she called:

> ' ... no other landscape than a monotonous street—of moorland, a grey church tower, rising from the centre of a churchyard so filled with graves that the rank weed and coarse grass scarce had room to shoot up between the monuments ...'
>
> (*Roe Head Journal* 1831–2)

is the ordinary, but also one of the most extraordinary, literary landscapes in the world.

The sisters – Anne, Emily and Charlotte – as painted by their brother, Branwell.
The 'pillar' space in this picture (now in the National Portrait Gallery) has been
shown by infra-red photography to have been originally occupied by a male
figure, probably Branwell himself. 'Emily's countenance struck me as full of
power; Charlotte's of solicitude; Anne's of tenderness' (Mrs Gaskell's *Life*,
Chapter 7)

The Brontës have fascinated biographers and literary critics from
their day to ours and will go on doing so. How did those three apparently
unremarkable sisters living a retired life in Haworth succeed in
producing the memorable works that bear their names? That question is
asked with greater pathos but also with greater certainty of answer when
one remembers the circumstances of their lives. Out of their own
suffering they portrayed suffering.

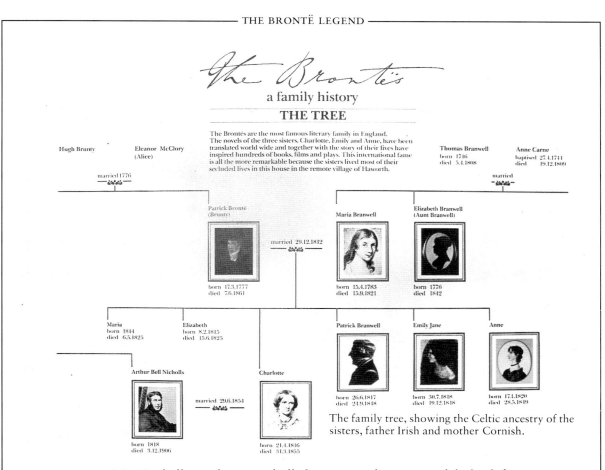

The Brontës

a family history

THE TREE

The Brontës are the most famous literary family in England. The novels of the three sisters, Charlotte, Emily and Anne, have been translated world wide and together with the story of their lives have inspired hundreds of books, films and plays. This international fame is all the more remarkable because the sisters lived most of their secluded lives in this house in the remote village of Haworth.

Hugh Brunty · Eleanor McClory (Alice)

married 1776

Thomas Branwell
born 1746
died 5.4.1808

Anne Carne
baptised 27.4.1744
died 19.12.1809

married

Patrick Brontë (Brunty)
born 17.3.1777
died 7.6.1861

married 29.12.1812

Maria Branwell
born 15.4.1783
died 15.9.1821

Elizabeth Branwell (Aunt Branwell)
born 1776
died 1842

Maria
born 1814
died 6.5.1825

Elizabeth
born 8.2.1815
died 15.6.1825

Patrick Branwell
born 26.6.1817
died 24.9.1848

Emily Jane
born 30.7.1818
died 19.12.1848

Anne
born 17.1.1820
died 28.5.1849

Arthur Bell Nicholls
born 1818
died 3.12.1906

married 29.6.1854

Charlotte
born 21.4.1816
died 31.3.1855

The family tree, showing the Celtic ancestry of the sisters, father Irish and mother Cornish.

Mrs Gaskell, to whom we shall always owe the greatest debt both for our knowledge of, and sympathy with, the Brontës, found their story almost unbearable when she first heard it. Coming to know Charlotte well in the last five years of the latter's life, she had no hesitation in accepting the commission to write her biography. In recounting that history she was moved both to pity and indignation as she recalled what those sisters had gone through. Her information may not always have been accurate. It may, however, have been truer than either she or we can ever prove. Mr Brontë, after reading the work, eventually protested against its account of his eccentricities, but if Mary Taylor, Charlotte's friend, had cared to tell more than she did and Mrs Gaskell had dared to print it, he would have come out worse than he did. And, whatever the truth about the girls' experience at school at Cowan Bridge and whatever the truth about Branwell's association with Mrs Robinson, the narration of both of which experiences brought threats of legal action on Mrs Gaskell's head, there is no doubt that what she said the Brontës themselves thought to be the truth. There can therefore be no questioning of the emotional effects that those events had upon them.

Then, given their motherless condition and the isolation of their lives

Haworth Moors under snow
– a scene familiar to and
loved by the Brontë sisters.

in that grey parsonage, thrown intensely upon themselves and with those vivid imaginations, deriving from their Celtic ancestry, quickly expressing themselves, the sisters fascinate by their unusual condition of heredity, environment and action. The products of that background from their early years—the so-called 'little writings'—are known about but not widely read. But who needs these when we have that terrible portrayal of the passions which came from Emily, imaginatively the strongest of them all and as unsparing of herself as the characters she delineated? Charlotte recognized the massive achievement and the massive effort it had required. Speaking still of her sister as a man under the pseudonym 'Ellis Bell', she wrote in the 1850 Preface:

> '*Wuthering Heights* was hewn in a wild workshop, with simple tools, out of homely materials. The statuary found a granite block on a solitary moor: gazing thereon, he saw how from the crag might be elicited the head, savage, swart, sinister; a form moulded with at least one element of grandeur—power.'

That power makes *Wuthering Heights* unique among novels. It asks us to go through an experience that only the most terrifying drama requires. It has been, not unaptly, compared with *King Lear*.

The mid nineteenth-century reviewers were uncomfortable with both *Wuthering Heights* and *Jane Eyre*. Even *Agnes Grey* with its candid portrayal of the lot of governesses also touched too tender a spot for some of them, whilst Anne's other novel, *The Tenant of Wildfell Hall*, was much too explicit in describing the ravages of alcohol. The reviewers called them 'vulgar' novels. None of these works knows compromise or understatement. In consequence, the mainly middle-class readers were uneasy—forced to recognize but unable to fit the impression of the novels into the pattern of their own experience, standards or expectations. Lockwood in *Wuthering Heights*, that rather effete Southerner, who, like the ancient mariner, has to tell the strange story he has heard, is in a way symbolic of that readership—profoundly disturbed by what he saw, unable to measure it, wishing he had never got mixed up in it, but yet fascinated and compelled by it.

Nobody before had written like the Brontës; nobody since has written like them. In due time it was revealed that nobody had lived like them. Out of their books and their lives the Brontë legend took its birth.

1. Patrick Brontë Comes to Yorkshire

In December 1809 the Reverend John Buckworth, Vicar of Dewsbury, obtained a new curate. He was the Reverend Patrick Brontë, who had already served in that capacity first to Joseph Jowett, Professor of Civil Law at Cambridge and non-resident vicar of Wethersfield (Essex), and then briefly at Wellington (Shropshire) where he met William Morgan, a fellow curate, and John Fennell, a local headmaster, who were both to figure later in the Brontë story.

Patrick Brontë had come a long way to Dewsbury—from Drumbally-roney, in fact, an Irish village sheltering beneath the Mountains of Mourne. He was the eldest of ten children, born on St Patrick's Day (17 March) 1777, precocious son of a peasant farmer, Brunty (or even Prunty). Patrick was apprenticed to a blacksmith, worked as a linen weaver, and by the time he was sixteen had taken up teaching, shortly to be engaged as tutor by Thomas Tighe, vicar of Drumgooland. This was the time of the Evangelical Revival with its emphasis on fervent personal religious commitment. Tighe was a Protestant, so was Patrick. Tighe had known and been influenced by John Wesley. Tighe saw Patrick Brunty's potential and was instrumental in getting him to Cambridge, a journey, it is said, that, apart from the sea-crossing, Patrick undertook entirely on foot.

That was in September 1802 and on 1 October his name was duly entered as 'Patrick Branty' in the books of St John's College, Cambridge. What a transformation—from the poverty of peasant surroundings in his homeland to the venerable cloisters of an ancient university! Two days later Patrick changed the registration from 'Branty' to 'Bronte', which progressively moved to 'Bronté' and then 'Brontë'. From Irish brogue to Italian overtones! And was not the most celebrated sailor of the day, Lord Nelson, also Duke of Brontë?

Mist and loneliness:
Warley Moor above
Luddendenfoot.
'I dream of moor, and misty
hill,
Where evening closes dark
 and chill'
Emily Brontë,
'The winter wind . . .'

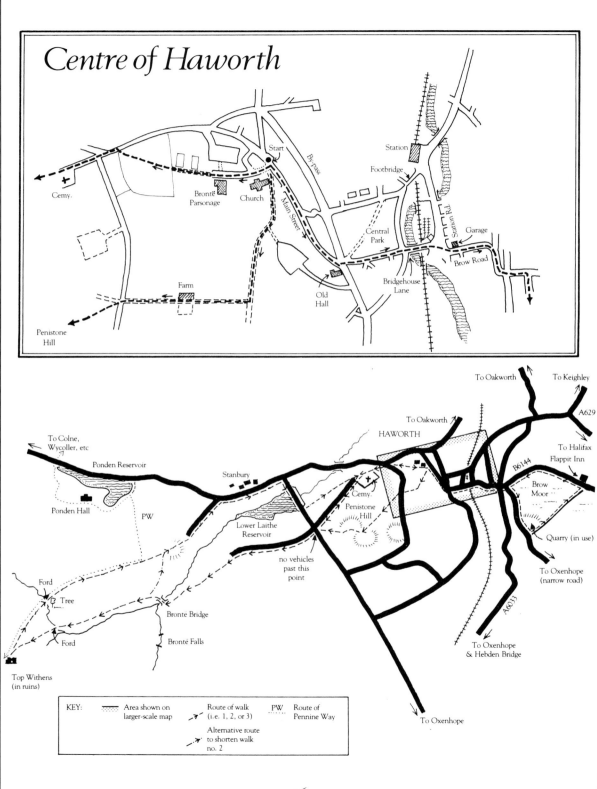

Centre of Haworth

Cemy.

Brontë Parsonage

Church

Start

By-pass

Main Street

Station

Footbridge

Central Park

Station Rd.

Garage

Brow Road

Bridgehouse Lane

Old Hall

Farm

Penistone Hill

To Oakworth

To Keighley

A629

To Oakworth

HAWORTH

To Halifax

Flappit Inn

B6144

Brow Moor

To Colne, Wycoller, etc

Ponden Reservoir

Stanbury

Cemy.

Penistone Hill

Ponden Hall

PW

Lower Laithe Reservoir

no vehicles past this point

Quarry (in use)

To Oxenhope (narrow road)

Ford

Tree

Brontë Bridge

A6033

To Oxenhope & Hebden Bridge

Ford

Brontë Falls

Top Withens (in ruins)

To Oxenhope

KEY: ───── Area shown on larger-scale map

Route of walk (i.e. 1, 2, or 3)

PW Route of Pennine Way

Alternative route to shorten walk no. 2

The determination that had brought Patrick to Cambridge saw him through Cambridge. He was a sizar, that is, a poor student in receipt of college assistance—a Hare Exhibition and a Duchess of Suffolk Exhibition, in return for which he was required to perform various menial and coaching duties. In addition to this help he also received assistance from the Church Missionary Society—twenty pounds per year, but coming, in fact, from those two renowned Evangelical notables, Henry Thornton and William Wilberforce. Patrick graduated BA in April 1806 and was ordained in August of that year.

If Cambridge was such a change after Ireland, Dewsbury after Wethersfield and even after Wellington must have been as great a shock. From the sleepy rural south of the Essex countryside where he had met and jilted Mary Burder, Patrick Brontë came to a busy woollen district where looms rattled for more hours of the day than they were still. He came to an area where factories and cottages had sprung up in unplanned profusion in the eighteenth century, of which in 1757 with somewhat wry perspective the minor poet John Dyer could speak thus:

> 'Behold, in Calder's vale, where wide around
> Unnumber'd villas creep the shrubby hills . . . .
> The sprightly scene, where many a busy hand,
> Where spoles, cards, wheels and looms, with motion quick,
> And ever murmuring sound, th'unwonted sense
> Wrap in surprise . . . . The younger hands
> Ply at the easy work of winding yarn
> On swiftly circling engines, and their notes
> Warble together, as a choir of larks . . . .
> . . . Take we now our eastward course
> To the rich fields of Burstal. Wide around,
> Hillock and valley, farm and village smile,
> And ruddy roofs, and chimney tops appear,
> Of busy Leeds, up-wafting to the clouds
> The incense of thanksgiving.'

(*The Fleece*, Book III)

It is highly unlikely that the inhabitants themselves regarded the smoke-laden atmosphere in quite such terms. Nor was pollution the only problem. The introduction of new machinery—and with it the possible displacement of labour, especially that of the croppers[1]—led to the Luddite riots of 1811–12. Charlotte Brontë was to make these central to the action of *Shirley*, and no doubt what she wrote then owed much to what she had learned from her father of that time and those events.

[1] Croppers cut the nap off cloth with large shears. One machine could do the work of ten men operating by hand.

St Peter's Church, Hartshead, Patrick Brontë's first independent charge, stands high on the moor, some four miles from what was then its 'mother'-church at Dewsbury. One of his predecessors there had been Hammond Roberson, a truly militant Evangelical.

West Yorkshire was a stronghold of Anglican Evangelicalism. Henry Venn, saintly pioneer of the movement, had been vicar of Huddersfield. The Elland Society—then, and later, a gathering of like-minded clergy—served as a means of fellowship for the Evangelicals of the area. In Dewsbury itself Matthew Powley had preceded John Buckworth as vicar. Prominent also over forty years in the area was another Evangelical, Hammond Roberson, one of Patrick's predecessors at Dewsbury and Hartshead, who was to be portrayed in Charlotte's *Shirley*.

From ministering at the parish church of Dewsbury Patrick Brontë moved to the curacy of Hartshead where, after protracted preliminaries, he was inducted in July 1811. He had moved up the hill out of the valley of the Calder which runs through Dewsbury and which was probably then and was certainly later the filthiest river in England. At Hartshead he ministered in the ancient parish church of St Peter for three years.

What was Patrick Brontë like in these years? We are accustomed to envisage the old man of stern, even gloomy, appearance from the well-known portrait; and from the impression conveyed by Mrs Gaskell we

The Old Bell Chapel, Thornton was a plain rectangular building, its only decoration the small octagonal bell-tower still to be seen among the ruins. Inside, like so many churches before so-called Victorian restorations, including Haworth itself, it had three-decker pulpit and box pews. Five of the Brontë children were baptized here.

get a sense of his idiosyncratic and irascible behaviour. One who knew some who were able to recall the curate of Dewsbury and Hartshead records that 'he was noted for his winning way with children, and for his stiff manner with the *nouveaux riches*.' (J A Erskine Stuart, *The Brontë Country*, 1888, p 33) He was powerfully built and a 'very handsome fellow, full of Irish enthusiasm, and with something of an Irishman's capability of falling easily in love.' (*Life*, Chapter 3) Patrick Brontë did fall in love—with Maria Branwell, a Cornish girl from Penzance, who was staying with her aunt and uncle, the Fennells, at Woodhouse Grove School, Apperley Bridge, near Bradford. Patrick had gone there in June 1812 with his former Wellington colleague, William Morgan, now curate of Bradford Parish Church, who was engaged to Jane Fennell. We know all too little of Maria Brontë, but what she went through in the remaining years of her short life evokes our sympathies. She came of a Calvinistic Methodist family but, though the severity of that persuasion is said to have been displayed by her sister, Elizabeth, the Brontë children's 'Aunt Branwell', no speck of its dark shadow has ever been associated with Maria. She was apparently, like her daughters, extremely small in build—'not pretty, but very elegant,' says Mrs Gaskell 'and always dressed with a quiet simplicity of taste which accorded well with her general character.' (*Life*, Chapter 3)

Maria was then about thirty and, as she put it, 'for some years I have been perfectly my own mistress, subject to no control whatever.' She goes on to note that her sisters, and even her mother, deferred to her superior wisdom, and immediately recognizes that this may seem boastful. She adds therefore:

> 'But you must consider that I do not boast of it. I have many times felt it a disadvantage, and although, I thank God, it has never led me into error, yet, in circumstances of uncertainty and doubt, I have deeply felt the want of a guide and instructor.'
>
> (*Life*, Chapter 3)

This comes from one of some nine of her surviving letters to Patrick Brontë. He showed them to Charlotte when she alone was left of all the children. Of them she commented in a letter to Ellen Nussey of 16 February 1850:

> 'The papers were yellow with time: . . . it was strange now to peruse the records of a mind whence my own sprang; and most strange, and at once sad and sweet, to find that mind of a truly fine, pure and elevated order . . . . There is a rectitude, a constancy, a modesty, a sense, a gentleness about them indescribable. I wished that she had lived, and that I had known her . . . .'

The birthplace at Thornton, Patrick Brontë's second living. In this unimposing terraced house, built in 1802, were born Charlotte, Branwell, Emily and Anne.

The letters show more than that, however. They show the liveliness and happiness of her brief courtship with her dear 'saucy Pat'. Patrick Brontë and Maria Branwell were married in a double ceremony with William Morgan and Jane Fennell at Guiseley Parish Church on 29 December 1812, each bridegroom officiating at the marriage of the other couple.

The Brontës set up house at Clough Lane, Hightown, below the heights of Hartshead and on the way to Dewsbury. They went there in January 1813; their eldest daughter, Maria, was born there in January 1814, and their second daughter, Elizabeth, in February 1815. A month later Patrick exchanged the living of Hartshead for that of Thornton (near Bradford), where the remaining Brontë children were born— Charlotte (21 April 1816), Patrick Branwell (26 June 1817), Emily Jane (30 July 1818) and Anne (17 January 1820). The family moved to Haworth in April 1820 and within eighteen months Maria Brontë was dead of cancer. Her last words were, 'Oh, God, my poor children—oh, God, my poor children.'

This ill-fortuned family had suffered its first cruel blow. Patrick was left with these six children, the eldest merely seven years of age. The stricken father with what even in his circumstances may appear consummate haste proposed marriage to Anne's godmother, Elizabeth Firth of Thornton—and was rejected. In 1823 he turned to his old love, Mary Burder of Wethersfield. But hell hath no fury like a woman scorned and all Patrick got for his trouble was a letter in which Miss Burder thanked God for a lucky escape, or to put it in hers and the language of the time:

'This review, Sir, excites in my bosom increased gratitude and thankfulness to that wise, that indulgent Providence which then watched over me for good and withheld me from forming in very early life an indissoluble engagement with one whom I cannot think was altogether clear of duplicity.'

With what Margaret Lane in *The Brontë Story* (1969 edn p 48) has described as 'pious nastiness' Miss Burder concludes of Patrick's and his family's afflicted condition: 'The Lord can supply all your and their need.' Thus Mary Burder passes out of the Brontë story, some years later to become Mrs Sibree.

And so Patrick Brontë settled down to forty long years of widowerhood—with Elizabeth Branwell, his wife's sister ('Aunt Branwell'), to care for the growing family and to remain in residence at Haworth until her own death in 1842. This elder spinster sister of Maria Brontë seems to have had none of the warmth or charm that had so obviously attracted Patrick to the younger woman. She responded nobly

Elizabeth, 'Aunt Branwell', a silhouette of unknown date. She was Maria Brontë's older sister, and, despite her forbidding character, looked after the motherless Brontës for the rest of her life punctiliously.

to the needs of Patrick Brontë and his stricken family, but there is never any suggestion that she liked it or that they much liked her. Certainly the servants did not. Nancy Garrs, who helped to nurse the children, complained that Aunt Branwell was:

> '. . . so crosslike and fault-findin' and so close, she ga'e us, my sister Sarah and me, but a gill of beer a day, and she gi'e it hessel', did Miss Branwell, to our dinner, she wouldn't let us go draw it oursel' in t' cellar. A pint a day she gi'e us, that were half a pint for me an' half a pint for Sarah.'
> (Helen H Arnold 'The Reminiscences of Emma Huidekoper Cortazzo: A friend of Ellen Nussey', *Brontë Society Transactions*, 1958, Vol 13)

That was before Methodism got itself enmeshed with teetotal allegiances, or they might have had to be content with less appetizing beverages.

But if there were those in Yorkshire who liked Aunt Branwell but

Wellington Parish Church, a plain classical building with Norman-type apse,
erected in 1790 and therefore quite new in Patrick Brontë's time as curate there.
Nearby was the town of Madeley, famous in Evangelical circles by the presence
of John Fletcher, whose widow is said to have recommended Patrick Brontë for a
curacy at Dewsbury.

Opposite above
Marsh Top (near Haworth).

Opposite below
Dewsbury Parish Church, where Patrick Brontë first ministered as curate to the
then vicar, John Buckworth. An ancient building with Saxon relics and medieval
glass, it was heavily restored in the 1880s. One of the main centres in Yorkshire of
Anglican Evangelicalism in the late eighteenth and early nineteenth centuries.

Haworth Moor – a
characteristic landscape
with rough tussocky grass,
uneven dry stone walls,
gaunt lone tree and solitary
building.

little, she in her turn had no love for Yorkshire. After Cornwall she found Haworth, according to Mrs Gaskell:

' ... a place where neither flowers nor vegetables would flourish, and where a tree of even moderate dimensions might be hunted for far and wide; where the snow lay long and late on the moors, stretching bleakly and barely far up from the dwelling which was henceforward to be her home; and where often, on autumnal or winter nights, the four winds of heaven seemed to meet and rage together, tearing round the house as if they were wild beasts striving to find an entrance. She missed the small round of cheerful, social visiting perpetually going on in a country town; she missed the friends she had known from her childhood, some of whom had been her parents' friends before they were hers; she disliked many of the customs of the place, and particularly dreaded the cold damp arising from the flag floors in the passages and parlours of Haworth Parsonage.'

(*Life*, Chapter 4)

Nevertheless, in conformity with her stern faith, she buckled down to what she regarded as her duty and imposed her discipline upon the domestic economy that had fallen to her care. Besides supervising the servants she instructed the children in sewing and religion. This she did from her bedroom where she seems to have spent most of her time in strict isolation. Her régime moved with military precision, and of its later years Mrs Gaskell has recorded:

'People in Haworth have assured me that, according to the hour of day—nay, the very minute—could they have told what the inhabitants of the parsonage were about. At certain times the girls would be sewing in their aunt's bedroom—the chamber which, in former days, before they had outstripped her in their learning, had served them as a school-room; at certain (early) hours they had their meals; from six to eight, Miss Branwell read aloud to Mr Brontë; at punctual eight, the household assembled to evening prayers in his study; and by nine he, Miss Branwell, and Tabby, were all in bed.'

(*Life*, Chapter 8)

Opposite
St John's College, Cambridge from the Backs with the River Cam in the foreground. Patrick Brontë studied here from 1802–6 and here Wordsworth before him had looked on:
'Gowns grave or gaudy, doctors, students, streets,
Courts, cloisters, flocks of churches, gateways, towers.'
The Prelude (1850) III, 32–33
The 'Bridge of Sighs' was not built until 1831.

Mary Taylor called her 'a very precise person'.

Anne, perhaps because she was most amenable, seems to have been Aunt Branwell's favourite. She certainly imbibed, most obviously, some of that dreary Calvinism that marked her aunt's beliefs. In a poem addressed 'To Cowper', that ultimate Calvinist in that he believed he had been specifically elected to damnation, she wrote:

'The language of my inmost heart
   I traced in every line
My sins, *my* sorrows, hopes, and fears
   Were there—and only mine . . . .

[And] should thy darkest fears be true,
   If Heaven be so severe,
That such a soul as thine is lost,—
   Oh! how shall I appear?'

Charlotte, too, experienced a phase of Calvinistic anxiety around 1836, but both she and Anne passed through it safely. Their later theological position, as far as one can define it, seems indeed to be at the opposite end of the spectrum. They both embraced some sort of belief in universal salvation for all mankind.

Opposite above
View from the moors with Haworth in the middle distance. The village remains today much the same size as in the time of the Brontës.

Opposite below
Woodhouse Grove School where Patrick Brontë first met his future wife Maria Branwell, when he was visiting to examine the boys in religious education.

2. Haworth and the Parsonage

The Brontës' move from Thornton to Haworth was a move into bleaker country, up the hills and onto the moors of this outcrop of the Pennine Chain. Two miles they climbed from Thornton up to Denholme, the removal carts proceeding slowly on their way. Even in summer this road has a cheerless atmosphere, passing as it does through tracts of rough, bare sheep pasture. In winter it is reminiscent of the lands from which the Scandinavian settlers in the area had come—with plenty of snow; and that still lying when it has long disappeared from the fields below. It is land where the predominant colour for much of the year is not green, but dun brown and black, save when in summer the moors bloom purple with heather. That way the family came, as the traveller from Bradford still does who comes to Haworth, though nowadays in far greater comfort than was theirs. Abraham Holroyd, an early commentator, described the Brontë migration:

'Hour after hour passes, and they leave Old Allen, Flappit Spring and Braemoor behind, and late in the afternoon the inhabitants of the quiet village of Haworth behold them pass up their steepest of all streets, and halt at the door of the parsonage. Thus came the Brontës to Haworth, strangers among strangers.'
(*Currer Bell and Her Sisters*, 1887)

Characteristically, in the railway age Mrs Gaskell approached Haworth from another direction. Beginning her work on *The Life of Charlotte Brontë*, just after her friend and fellow novelist had died, she travelled by train from Manchester to Keighley and thence by road to Haworth. This was her impression:

The parsonage and the school seen from
the churchyard in winter.

'For two miles the road passes over tolerably level ground, distant
hills on the left, a 'beck' flowing through meadows on the right, and
furnishing water power, at certain points, to the factories built on its
banks. The air is dim and lightless with the smoke from all these
habitations and places of business. The soil in the valley (or
'bottom', to use the local term) is rich; but, as the road begins to
ascend, the vegetation becomes poorer; it does not flourish, it
merely exists; and, instead of trees, there are only bushes and shrubs
about the dwellings. Stone dykes are everywhere used in place of
hedges; and what crops there are, on the patches of arable land,
consist of pale, hungry-looking, grey-green oats. Right before the
traveller on this road rises Haworth village; he can see it for two
miles before he arrives, for it is situated on the side of a pretty steep
hill, with a background of dun and purple moors, rising and
sweeping away yet higher than the church, which is built at the very
summit of the long narrow street. All round the horizon there is this
same line of sinuous wave-like hills; the scoops into which they fall
only revealing other hills beyond, of similar colour and shape,
crowned with wild, bleak moors—grand, from the ideas of solitude

Haworth main street with its steep cobbled surface.

Old alleyway off Haworth main street.

and loneliness which they suggest, or oppressive from the feeling which they give of being pent-up by some monotonous and illimitable barrier, according to the mood of mind in which the spectator may be.'

(*Life*, Chapter 2)

How Mr Brontë came to find himself in Haworth is a story in itself. The census for 1821 records the inhabitants of this 'populous manufacturing village' as numbering 4668. They were a sturdy, independent, self-willed people, men who compelled the surroundings to yield them a living. To Mrs Gaskell who, though she had her 'Cranford' upbringing behind her, nonetheless knew the plain outspoken ways of Manchester workingmen, these West Riding folk were a :

'. . . wild, rough population. Their accost is curt; their accent and tone of speech is blunt and harsh . . . . Their feelings are not easily roused, but their duration is lasting. Hence there is much close friendship and faithful service . . . . From the same cause come also enduring grudges, in some cases amounting to hatred, which occasionally has been bequeathed from generation to generation.'

(*Life*, Chapter 2)

The presentation to the perpetual curacy of Haworth was full of acrimonious potential and in 1819 potential became actuality. The right of presentation lay with the vicar of Bradford, but the funds on which the clergyman's stipend largely depended were in the hands of local trustees who staunchly maintained their right not just to veto but even, it seems, to nominate. They turned away Patrick Brontë because he was the vicar of Bradford's choice, so then the vicar sent them Samuel Redhead who was somewhat less prudent than the Irishman the inhabitants of Haworth had first rejected and who then came to spend the rest of his life amongst them.

On his first appearance Redhead officiated in a full church or, more accurately, he began to do so, for at the beginning of the second lesson he was faced by a mass exit of the congregation, all clog-shod and 'clattering and clumping'. Next Sunday there was a variation of the resistance. Halfway through the service, face to tail and wearing several old hats, a man rode into church and round the aisles on a donkey. Screams, laughter and general pandemonium—and the premature end of yet another service. The persistent parson tried again, this time accompanied by friends from Bradford. The parishioners brought with them a soot-begrimed and drunken chimneysweep. 'They placed him right before the reading-desk, where his blackened face nodded a drunken, stupid assent

Samuel Redhead, the cleric so mistreated
by the parishioners of Haworth, later
became vicar of Calverley.

to all that Mr Redhead said.' (*Life*, Chapter 2) The climax came when the
sweep ascended the stairs of the old three-decker pulpit and embraced the
surprised cleric, black as the devil against the white of the surplice. To
complete the débâcle, the parishioners pursued the retreating pair out of
the church, hurled both of them into the soot the sweep had deposited,
and Redhead with his friends escaped not only further insult but also
possible serious injury by seeking refuge in the nearby Black Bull Inn.
That was the end of Samuel Redhead, so far as Haworth was concerned,
except that he did return to preach several years later when all trace of
malice had disappeared from both sides. Patrick Brontë came into his
own, acceptable to the independent parishioners of Haworth because of
his more circumspect behaviour towards them than had been that of his
would-be replacement.

So Patrick entered into residence at Haworth Parsonage and into
ministry at the church of St Michael and All Angels (not St Autest, as Mrs
Gaskell so unaccountably called it). Let her, however, describe the
approach up the village street, for, though in essentials much survives,

Opposite
Haworth Church today and, *above*, Haworth Church in Patrick Brontë's time.
His successor considerably altered the church, as was the fashion at the time,
calling it 'restoration', in that the mid-Victorian passion was for Elizabethan and
medieval styles, becoming known as Victorian Gothic.

Haworth Church and Parsonage. The frontispiece to Vol II of Mrs Gaskell's *Life
of Charlotte Brontë*.

she herself must remain the most reliable guide to the scene as it was actually known to Charlotte Brontë and her sisters:

> 'For a short distance the road appears to turn away from Haworth, as it winds round the base of the shoulder of a hill; but then it crosses a bridge over the 'beck', and the ascent through the village begins. The flag-stones with which it is paved are placed end-ways, in order to give a better hold to the horses' feet; and, even with this help, they seem to be in constant danger of slipping backwards. The old stone houses are high compared to the width of the street, which makes an abrupt turn before reaching the more level ground at the head of the village, so that the steep aspect of the place, in one part, is almost like that of a wall. But this surmounted, the church lies a little off the main road on the left; a hundred yards, or so, and the driver relaxes his care, and the horse breathes more easily, as they pass into the quiet little by-street that leads to Haworth Parsonage. The church-yard is on one side of this lane, the school-house and the sexton's dwelling (where the curates formerly lodged) on the other.'
>
> (Life, Chapter 2)

The church and the parsonage are, nowadays, much altered from what they were in Brontë times. After the fashion of the period Patrick Brontë's successor, the Reverend John Wade, changed things in the name of restoration and the old church with its open 'old meeting-house' interior, box-pews and three-decker pulpit, disappeared altogether, apart from the tower. Simplicity gave way to decoration. Now there is a building, consisting of the nave with six bays, north and south aisles of five, the chancel of three and side chapels of two. One of these (that on the south side) is now given over to the Brontës. The ornateness of the church comes from the Derbyshire alabaster panel of Da Vinci's *Last Supper* above the holy table, and the accompanying pulpit, font and altar screen made from the same material. As for the parsonage, it was doubtless too small for Mr Wade's needs and his extension has proved useful in accommodating exhibits since the house was taken over by the Brontë Society. The nice proportions of the original Georgian building are gone, but it is still possible with the mind's eye to imagine it without its Victorian excrescence.

Again Mrs Gaskell serves us well:

Opposite
The parsonage kitchen. Charlotte's 'History of the Year 1829' reads 'Tabby, the servant, is washing up the breakfast-things, and Anne, my youngest sister . . ., is kneeling on a chair, looking at some cakes which Tabby has been baking for us . . . Aunt is upstairs in her room, and I am sitting by the table writing this in the kitchen.'

Above
Mr Brontë's study with his portrait on the wall. Haworth Parsonage, now the
Brontë Museum, contains Brontë clothes and furniture, and incorporates the
Bonnell Collection, put together over thirty years by Henry Houston Bonnell of
Philadelphia.

Opposite above
The sitting-room in the parsonage with Richmond's portrait of Charlotte over
the mantelpiece.

Opposite below
Items on Charlotte's desk – steel pens did not come into use until the 1860s,
fountain pens in the 1890s.

The Black Bull Hotel by the church steps – a favourite haunt of Branwell's.

'The parsonage stands at right angles to the road, facing down upon the church; so that, in fact, parsonage, church and belfried schoolhouse, form three sides of an irregular oblong, of which the fourth is open to the fields and moors that lie beyond. The area of this oblong is filled up by a crowded churchyard, and a small garden or court in front of the clergyman's house. As the entrance to this from the road is at the side, the path goes round the corner into the little plot of ground. Underneath the windows is a narrow flower-border, carefully tended in days of yore, although only the most hardy plants could be made to grow there. Within the stone wall, which keeps out the surrounding churchyard, are bushes of elder and lilac; the rest of the ground is occupied by a square grass plot and a gravel walk. The house is of grey stone, two stories high, heavily roofed with flags, in order to resist the winds that might strip off a lighter covering. It appears to have been built about a hundred years ago, and to consist of four rooms on each story; the two windows on the right (as the visitor stands, with his back to the

Opposite above
The parsonage viewed from the churchyard, with the Victorian extension on the right largely obscured by trees.